917.8
C

C1

CHESTER, MICHAEL

FIRST WAGONS TO
CALIFORNIA

© THE BAKER & TAYLOR CO.

FIRST WAGONS
TO CALIFORNIA

In May, 1844, forty covered wagons set out from Council
Bluffs in the Iowa Territory for the first overland wagon trip
across country. It was the beginning of the historic journey
that opened California to the westward push of young America.

On the trip was Moses Schallenberger, a young man of seventeen. This is his story, too, as seen through his own memoirs —
the story of his tricks on John Sullivan, his meetings with the
Sioux and Otoe Indians, his lonely vigil through the long winter
months in the cabin east of the Sierra Nevada.

Michael Chester records this great adventure in a lively and
historically accurate narrative.

FIRST WAGONS
TO CALIFORNIA

by

Michael Chester

Illustrated by Steele Savage

Historical Consultant:
Edna B. Ziebold, San Diego Dept. of Education

G. P. PUTNAM'S SONS

NEW YORK

This book is dedicated to Perc Sapsis, a pioneer who came west in the forties.

Contents

FIRST WAGONS
TO CALIFORNIA

Introduction

IN THIS HISTORY of the overland trip to California in the year
1844, I have made every attempt to adhere to factual material.
The main source of my information is *The Opening of the California Trail*, by George R. Stewart, University of California
Press, 1953.

In his excellent and scholarly work Professor Stewart in-
cludes the old manuscript, "Overland in 1844," which is the
most important historical document concerning the expedition.
In that manuscript there are many allusions to Moses Schallenberger's original narrative, and one long passage quoted
directly from Schallenberger. The reader is referred to Professor
Stewart's work, in which he not only presents the entirety of

"Overland in 1844," but also presents a thorough commentary and detailed annotations.

During my senior year at the University of California at Berkeley, I was able to take Professor Stewart's course in creative writing. I recall that he provided a steadying influence on my development as an author. That was in the spring of 1952, and it was the approximate time of Professor Stewart's work on *The Opening of the California Trail.* Through the kinds of coincidence that play so large a role in any person's life, I found myself following his well-blazed trail eleven years later as I wrote this account of Moses Schallenberger and the others who came overland by covered wagon.

My departures from the factual material have been slight. Occasionally I have used brief bits of dialogue to enliven and clarify my narrative. But these dialogues are based on factual data regarding actions and feelings as stated in the memoirs of Moses Schallenberger. In several cases, dialogue recorded in the memoirs is quoted directly. Occasionally, too, I have taken minor liberties in describing scenes and events that are treated rather sketchily by Schallenberger. But for the most part, I have been fairly scrupulous in adhering to the historical material in this great adventure that took place in the year 1844.

— MICHAEL CHESTER

Sunnyvale, California

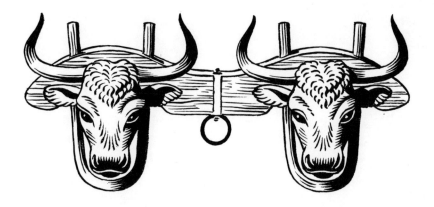

PART ONE

ACROSS COUNTRY

CHAPTER 1

Crossing the Missouri

ON THE EAST BANK of the Missouri River, near the town of
Council Bluffs in the Iowa Territory, the journey began. There,
in May, 1844, forty covered wagons were gathered at a camp-
site. The oxen were moving slowly about in a nearby field, grazing on the spring foliage. In the wagons, women were taking
care of babies and preparing meals. Near the wagons the men
were working, greasing the axles and kingbolts, and patching
the canvas wagon covers. There was reason for careful prepara-
tion — they were getting ready for a 2,000 mile trip to the west.

The boys helped their fathers by fetching tools, working on
the wagons, and collecting wood for the campfire. The girls

spent the time helping their mothers wash clothes and caring for the babies. In between chores, there were games near the camp: scouts-and-Indians, hide-and-seek, skimming rocks along the surface of the Missouri, and catching frogs. The boys and girls of the wagon train also enjoyed talking about the trip that lay ahead:

"Wonder if we'll see Indians."

"Maybe. The Sioux caught a scout from the Bartleson party and took away his guns and his mule."

"The Bartleson party had to leave their wagons behind and go on foot when they got to California."

"Yes, but they had mules. Mules don't pull strong."

"The heck they don't! My dad says that a mule —"

"— Anyway, all we have is oxen."

In their conversations they found that they were not all headed for the same destination. Most of the wagons were bound for Oregon. Eleven of the wagons were bound for California. The two expeditions would travel together across the Rocky Mountains to the Snake River. There, the main expedition would continue on the Oregon Trail, while the eleven California wagons would turn and head toward the southwest.

In one of the California wagons, there was a young man whose name was Moses Schallenberger. His fellow pioneers usually called him "Mose." Mose was seventeen years old at that time, and rather thin and scrawny. But he was a handsome boy, dark-haired, with bold, alert eyes, and with all the courage needed for a trip into the wilderness. He was traveling with his married sister and her husband, John Townsend, a country doctor. Mose's sister, Elizabeth, was a good deal older than

Mose; Elizabeth was in her thirties and had taken care of Mose ever since their parents died. Now, Mose was old enough to be on his own. Before the journey west was over, he was to prove himself as a man on more than one occasion.

At Council Bluffs, Mose wished sometimes that he were more like the Greenwood boys. The Greenwoods were not traveling with their older sister. They were with their father, a rugged, bearded old pioneer. Old Caleb Greenwood had lived for years with the Crow Indians, with a Crow squaw for his wife. The boys, John, twenty, and Britain, eighteen, were half-Crow, had been brought up among the Crow, and were as wild and unruly as timber wolves. Old Greenwood was to go along as guide for the California wagons, and his boys were to ride with him.

At the end of a hard day's work at the Council Bluffs camp-site, Mose lay beside Dr. Townsend's covered wagon, listening to the sound of crickets and night birds and watching the campfire, hearing the sizzle of bacon grease on the hot coals; watching his sister shaking out the wash with a snapping sound before she hung it up to dry on the side of the wagon; hearing the sound of a boy in the next wagon gagging as Dr. Townsend held his tongue down with a spoon; listening to the rushing waters of the Missouri River a hundred yards away, and smelling the wild, haunting smells of spring.

There was an air of adventure in the camp as they prepared for the trip. Many hundreds of miles of strange land lay ahead, and at the end of the journey was California, which they knew very little about. The people who were going on this trip were adventurers, more willing to face the dangers of the rugged west than to live a life of monotony; willing to risk life and limb,

15

willing to wear themselves to the bone in order to try their luck on the frontier.

At Council Bluffs, the pioneers elected a trail captain. The vote went to a silent, hawk-nosed blacksmith named Elisha Stevens. Stevens had no family with him — only his wagon and two hired men. He was not very sociable. He was like a figure carved out of stone, a man of few words, gnarly and broad-shouldered — a man who kept to himself. But he was a strong man and a good leader, and the other men knew that he was, so they chose him to be their captain.

With a captain elected, the pioneers were ready to start their journey. The first problem was the crossing of the Missouri.

The men built a raft and ferried the wagons across the river. The oxen were to swim across. But the current was so strong that the animals became frightened. When they were forced into the water, they swam in circles, struggling to climb onto each other's backs. The men gave up and let the terrified animals climb out again on the eastern bank. Some of the oxen became stuck in the mud and sank in so deeply that they had to be left there.

Finally two men crossed the river in a canoe, leading one of the tamest of the oxen behind them. The rest of the animals followed the lead ox, and they swam safely across.

As Mose helped to tie the oxen on the west bank of the river, he could think of only one thing: the great unknown lands to the west. He hoped that they would start on the trail very soon.

CHAPTER 2

A Trick on John Sullivan

IT WAS NOT LONG before Mose learned that about half the people going to California were named Murphy. The Murphy clan was led by old Mr. Martin Murphy, a gray-haired Irishman. With him were his sons and daughters, in-laws, and grandchildren. Of the forty-nine people bound for California, twenty-two were part of the Murphy family.

That night, with the oxen and wagons across the Missouri, most of the pioneers slept in the camp at Council Bluffs. But there were several who camped on the far side of the river to guard the wagons. The western side of the Missouri was in the country of the Otoe Indians. The Otoes were not a warlike tribe, but they had a reputation for stealing. Elisha Stevens chose some sentries to keep an eye on the oxen and the wagons. And he picked two of the younger men as "corporals of the guard," to move from sentry post to sentry post, to make sure that the sentries were awake and that all was well. Mose was chosen as one of the two corporals. His partner was a boy his own age, a laughing, reckless youth named John Murphy.

The wagons were parked in a big circle, with the tongue* of each wagon resting beneath the rear axle of the wagon in front of it. In that way the wagons formed the kind of corral that was used when pioneers defended themselves against Indian raids. The oxen were tied up just outside the corral.

As Mose and John Murphy began their patrol, it was beginning to get dark. In the surrounding dimness, they could hear the hooting of owls. Mose wondered whether the hoots might be Indians signaling to each other.

At first, the patrol was fun. The boys were armed with shotguns, and they kept their eyes open for Indians. From time to time, they stopped to chat with the sentries at the posts. Then, as the hours went on, they began to get bored. They were supposed to take turns sleeping, but it was too early to sleep.

"I've got an idea, Mose," said John Murphy, talking in a half whisper so that the nearby sentry would not hear him. "Let's give Sullivan a scare."

"Who's Sullivan?"

"He's the tenderfoot in that wagon there. He's scared that the Indians are going to take his scalp."

"What do you want to do?" asked Mose.

* The long wooden pole at the front of a covered wagon, running between the oxen and attached to their harnesses

"Well, we could hide his oxen and tell him the Indians took them."

"Maybe. But we'll probably get in trouble with your brother if we do." Mose was talking about John's oldest brother, Martin. Martin Murphy Junior was not a boy, he was 37 years old, and one of the leaders of the wagon train. Martin was in charge of the wagons that night, because Captain Stevens was spending the night on the east bank with the main party.

John Murphy nodded. "Sure, we don't want to get Martin all riled at us. I'll tell you what — let's let him in on the secret ahead of time. If I know him, he'll enjoy it himself."

When the boys found Martin, he was leaning against the edge of his wagon, talking with Old Greenwood. "What's the trouble, lads?" asked Martin.

John Murphy rested his shotgun on the wagon tongue. "I'll tell you what, Marty, we were fixing to play a trick on Sullivan." And he told his brother about their plan.

Martin Murphy laughed. "Now isn't that a fine thing to be doing? Getting poor John Sullivan up in the dead of night to chase after oxen." And he laughed again. Even Old Greenwood cackled with merriment.

That was all that John Murphy and Mose needed to hear. They stole quickly out into the darkness where John Sullivan's white oxen were staked for the night, and untied the halters.

Then, as quietly as they could, they drove the oxen a few hundred yards away from the camp. They came back to camp, struggling to hold back their laughter, awoke John Sullivan, and told him that the Indians had stolen his oxen.

John Sullivan leaped into his trousers, seized a rifle, and rushed out into the darkness. Finally, as he peered through the darkness, he sighted the white shapes of his oxen, moving slowly about in the distance. Keeping a wary eye open for Indians, he rounded up the oxen. John Murphy and Mose helped him in the roundup, and they pretended to stare anxiously about them too, to see if Indians were coming.

No sooner had John Sullivan tied up his oxen and gone back to sleep than the boys shook him awake once more. "They're gone again, John, the oxen are gone again," shouted the boys. Then, they doubled up with laughter as they watched him go charging into the night. This time they had taken the oxen even farther away than before.

Poor John Sullivan wandered about, searching for his oxen, and muttering about the thieving Otoes. John Murphy and Mose hid nearby, laughing under their breaths until their ribs ached.

Finally, John Sullivan stood on top of a fallen tree trunk to see if he could spot his herd. From his hiding place, John Murphy pointed his shotgun at the sky and fired. John Sullivan leaped from the trunk and ran back to the wagons, shouting, "Indians, Indians, they're on the warpath." Meanwhile, John Murphy and Mose rounded up the oxen and brought them back again.

The next morning, everyone was talking about the night's excitement. Captain Elisha Stevens had come across the river, and he stood, silent, fierce, and hawklike, as Martin Murphy explained that there had been no real trouble with Otoe Indians. In fact, nobody had seen any sign of the Otoes. Then Martin told Captain Stevens what had really happened.

Captain Stevens sent for John Murphy and Mose. "Good work, boys," said Captain Stevens. "That was very brave of you to bring back those oxen. Twice in one night."

John Murphy and Mose did not know what to say. So they said nothing.

With a wink at the boys, Captain Stevens said, "I wonder why those Otoes kept taking Sullivan's oxen — other people had oxen tied out there."

John Murphy grinned. "I guess because his are white," he said. "The Indians could see them better in the dark."

As for John Sullivan, he believed until his dying day that the Otoes had tried to steal his oxen, and he often told people about his close call among the Indians.

In a way, it was a foolish trick. Certainly, it was unkind, and it was dangerous for John Murphy to be firing his shotgun into the air to frighten John Sullivan. If John Sullivan had seen one of the boys in hiding, he might have mistaken him for an Indian and fired a shot at him.

But it was a wilder, younger time in history, and a pair of boys, setting out on a great journey into the wilderness, were likely to do something foolish once in a while.

Two days later the pioneers left the Missouri River and headed westward toward the Elkhorn River. There the men made a ferryboat by taking one of the wagons apart and covering its wooden bed with rawhide to make it watertight. Then the other wagons were taken apart and were ferried across the Elkhorn piecemeal, to be put together again on the far side. As for swimming the cattle across, that was no hard trick this time. The men had already solved that problem.

After they had crossed the Elkhorn, they set out across the prairies north of the river Platte. At the front of the big expedition were the eleven California wagons. Alongside rode the three Greenwoods. The dust rose from the hooves of the oxen as they pulled the wagons, and the shouts of the oxen drivers could be heard. Many of the pioneers were on horseback, some of them riding herd on the spare oxen. These spare oxen were important as reserve wagon teams and also as meat on the hoof.

Everything was going well, and nobody could have guessed at the hardships ahead. Certainly, Mose could not have foreseen the grim struggles that he would have to face, all alone, in a distant mountain range. Now, there was only the feeling of success and the comforting sound of the creaking wheels and the lowing oxen and the horses' hoofbeats. They were on the road to California.

CHAPTER 3

The Prairie

THE PIONEERS were no longer among the Otoes. They were in the lands of the warlike Sioux nation. The Sioux Indians had a reputation for fierce raids and scalping parties. As the wagons moved across the plains, John Sullivan was not the only man who glanced warily toward the horizon to see if the Sioux were coming.

One day, after they crossed the Elkhorn, they came to a ruined Indian village. It was a Pawnee village that had been raided by a large Sioux war party. Only women, children, and very old men were left alive in the Pawnee village. All the braves of the village had been killed by the Sioux. This ruined scene left a grim impression on the pioneers as they continued across the prairie. There were still more than 400 miles between them and Fort Laramie. At any place within those 400 miles, there was the possibility that they would meet the Sioux.

The trail to Fort Laramie led westward along the Platte River. Before reaching Fort Laramie, the pioneers had to cross the entire area that is now the state of Nebraska.

The trip along the Platte was peaceful. Even though everyone was on the lookout for the Sioux, all they saw were herds of buffalo. The first buffalo they found were a few old bulls that had been driven from the herd by younger, stronger bulls. The boys of the wagon train were so excited by a chance to shoot some buffalo that they opened fire on one of these bulls while he was near the wagon train. He charged the train, and dropped within fifty feet of the wagons with about twenty bullets in him. But the meat of this old bull was tough and poor. Later, the pioneers caught up with the main herd. Then the hunters brought back good meat.

It was a little over a month between the time that the pioneers left Council Bluffs and the time that they arrived, weary and dusty, at the gates of Fort Laramie.

There was a surprise in store for them as they rounded the last bend before the fort. Thousands of Sioux Indians were camped between them and the fort. John Sullivan must have had quite a scare. And he was probably not the only one who did.

However, it was not a Sioux war party. The Sioux braves had their squaws and papooses with them. They would not be looking for trouble in that situation. In fact, they had come to Fort Laramie in order to trade.

Fort Laramie in the 1840s was a strange and colorful place. It was not yet a United States Army post — the army took possession of the fort some years later, in 1849.

Old Fort Laramie was a trading post, where trappers and other traders did business with the Indians and with pioneers on the Oregon Trail. But trading posts in the old west were

built as forts, and usually had the word "fort" as part of their names. Fort Laramie was one of several fortified trading posts scattered through that wild country. There was good reason to fortify a trading post, with the Sioux Indians as next-door neighbors.

The big wooden gate of Fort Laramie was raised, and the wagon train moved inside. As he rode into the fort on horseback, Mose looked up and saw a sentry perched in the blockhouse that rose over the gateway. Long, low buildings stretched out in a large circle, forming the walls of the fort.

The great open area inside the fort was crowded with Indian chiefs in white buffalo hides bargaining with bearded traders. Other Indians lay on the low roofs of the adobe buildings and stared down at the newly arrived pioneers in the wagon train. Squaws in bright robes looked longingly at beads held out by the traders. Lean, rough-looking frontiersmen strolled among the Indians, holding their long rifles, alert for any sign of trouble. Mules, horses, and oxen grazed on the grass inside the fort. A broken-down covered wagon was parked near one side of the fort, one wheel almost twisted off. Mose wondered how long it had been there, and who had left it.

The most important part of life at Fort Laramie seemed to be the trading. Leather hides, furs, jugs, knives, and beads were passed between Indians and traders, as they bargained.

The wagon train stayed at Fort Laramie for several days. Everyone had a good rest, and the horses and oxen grazed on the long grass. Mose and John Murphy wandered about the fort, exploring the blockhouse and the adobe buildings.

Perhaps Mose's brother-in-law, Dr. Townsend, had the most

fun of all. Dr. Townsend was a man who enjoyed trades and business deals. Mose watched him bargaining with the traders over horses and furs. Encouraged by the doctor, the other pioneers joined in the trading. The main trades they made were to exchange their tired horses for fresh, muscular Indian ponies, and their worn-out boots for moccasins.

As they left Fort Laramie, the pioneers kept their wagons in close formation. They were deep in Sioux territory now, and they were leaving the fort farther and farther behind. Captain Stevens gave the order that there would be no fires after dark, because the Sioux might see the light from far away and attack.

But one of the men from the Oregon wagons disobeyed the order. His name was Mr. Derby. He was an angry old gentleman who did not like to be told what to do. The first night that the order was given, he kept his fire burning after dark.

Dr. Townsend was in charge of the night watch at the time. When he saw Mr. Derby crouched by a blazing campfire, he was very angry. "Put out that fire, sir," said the doctor. "Haven't you heard the captain's orders?"

Mr. Derby peered defiantly up at the doctor. "Captain Stevens is an old granny. I'm not putting my fire out for him. And not for anybody else either."

Dr. Townsend got very red in the face, and grabbing a stick, he scattered the burning logs and scraped ashes and dust over the hot coals until the fire was gone. Mr. Derby watched silently, pale and trembling with fury.

Dr. Townsend strode away to patrol the wagons. A few minutes later, he glanced back toward Mr. Derby's wagon. The fire was blazing again. Dr. Townsend walked back to the fire and stared angrily down at the defiant old man. "Put out your fire, Derby," said the doctor.

"No, I won't," said Mr. Derby. "And it won't be healthy for anyone else to try it."

Dr. Townsend grabbed a stick once more and scattered the burning logs for yards around, kicking dust and ashes on them, and stamping on the coals, until not a spark was burning. Then he turned to Mr. Derby, who was still crouching by the place where the fire used to be. "Sir," said the doctor, "you will be in serious trouble if you light that fire again tonight."

Something in Dr. Townsend's manner must have impressed the stubborn Mr. Derby, because he did not light his fire again that night. But the next morning, he complained to Captain Stevens that the doctor had mistreated him.

The captain knew the whole story already. He told Mr. Derby that he would have to do what he was told. There were to be no more night fires. The safety of everyone in the expedition depended on it.

Mr. Derby still felt that he was being mistreated. He said that he did not want to travel with the wagon train any longer. For a week, he camped a half mile behind the train, sulking in the darkness. Now that he was alone, he was too frightened of the Sioux to light his fire.

Then, one day, scouts brought in word that they had seen a band of Sioux horsemen in the distance. That night, Mr. Derby camped in the wagon train again. And he did not try to light a night fire. From that time on, he was an agreeable and obedient member of the wagon train.

MOSE'S FRIEND, John Murphy, had been sick for several days, bedded down in one of the several Murphy wagons. Mose missed his friend, but he had something else to interest him. Allen Montgomery, a friend of Dr. Townsend, was the gunsmith of the wagon train. In his spare time, Allen had made a pair of fine pistols for Mose. When he had nothing else to do, Mose would clean and oil his pistols and take them apart and put them together again. He was very proud of these beautiful weapons.

Finally, John Murphy was over his fever. As soon as he was

well, John was ready for more adventure, and he asked Mose if he wanted to go hunting.

Mose thought it was a good idea. The wagon train had camped for a few days because the oxen were tired. It was boring to stay around the wagons all the time. Besides, supplies were running a little low, and if they could bring back some buffalo meat, they would be helping out a great deal.

"Now, where are you lads off to?" asked Martin Murphy, when he saw the two boys about to leave the camp.

"We're going to bring back some buffalo meat," said Mose proudly.

"With the appetite of the two of you, you'll have it eaten before you get back," said Martin.

John Murphy turned in his saddle and called back to his brother, "We'll save you the liver, Marty."

The boys rode slowly away from the wagons through the tall grass with their rifles ready. And Mose had his two new pistols strapped on his belt. But at first, their weapons were of no use to them, for they saw neither buffalo nor any other game. Then, as they stopped to let their horses drink at a creek, Mose saw something moving, far in the distance — something dark, near the horizon. It was a herd of buffalo.

The buffalo were not as easy to shoot as Mose and John thought they would be. The herd-bulls, stationed on high ground, sounded a warning whenever the hunters came close. Hearing the warning bellow, the herd would break and run several hundred yards away. After many hours of riding after the buffalo, Mose and John decided to give up. By that time, it was almost sunset.

As the boys rode back to the wagon train, they passed herds of antelope. But they were embarrassed about bringing back a small bony antelope, when they had boasted about going after buffalo. Then, John Murphy began to think that an antelope was better than nothing. The antelope came so close to them that John said he might shoot one in self-defense to make sure he did not get bitten. And finally, he lifted his rifle and brought down one of the bigger ones.

"There's not much meat on him," said Mose, "but every little bit helps."

Mose and John dismounted next to the slain antelope. "We'd better carve him up," said John.

"I guess," said Mose. "Though there's hardly enough meat on him to feed a healthy man."

The boys put their rifles down in the grass and started to work, skinning and carving the antelope meat. Meanwhile, their horses began to stray. When Mose looked around, the horses were grazing a few hundred yards away. He slipped off his gun belt that held the brace of pistols, a shot pouch and a powder horn, so that he could move more easily. "I'll get them, Johnny." He started after the horses, moving slowly in order not to frighten them. Without much difficulty, he caught hold of the bridles and started to lead the horses back to where John Murphy was still at work on the antelope. Then Mose noticed that the blanket was missing from John's horse. He called John to help look for it.

After a few minutes of searching, they found the blanket. Then they started to lead the horses back to the antelope so that they could finish their work. But they could not find the antelope. It was hidden by the high grass. As they stared about them, in all directions, all they could see was grass — thousands of acres. Somewhere in that grass was the slain antelope. And next to it lay their rifles, and Mose's gunbelt with the two pistols. They searched until it was dark. One place in the tall grass looked much like another. Mose could think of only one thing — the two fine pistols that Allen Montgomery had made for him, fashioning the barrels over the fire, with his brow furrowed, and his skillful hands gripping the bellows and the fire tongs. Mose could hardly bear the idea of telling Allen about the lost pistols.

John Murphy, as usual, had an idea. Instead of telling everyone how they had lost the antelope and the guns, why not tell them that they had been captured by Indians, and that the Indians had taken away their guns and then set them free. That way, they could save themselves a great deal of embarrassment.

Mose wasn't sure that he liked that idea. It was bad enough

to lose the guns without going back and getting everyone worried about imaginary Indians.

Finally, the boys decided to tell the truth. But arriving in camp with neither game nor guns, after their boasting, was very embarrassing. Confessing his foolishness to the grave, bearded faces of Dr. Townsend and Elisha Stevens was probably one of the hardest things that Mose had ever done. But he felt worst of all whenever he thought of Allen Montgomery and all the time Allen had spent making the pistols.

The next day, before the wagon train started on the trail again, Mose and John went back and searched for several hours through the grass. But the guns were not to be found. Perhaps they are still lying there, somewhere in the state of Wyoming, hidden by the tall grass, or covered by earth.

CHAPTER 4

The Sioux

As SUPPLIES ran low, Elisha Stevens and the other leaders decided that buffalo meat would have to be the main food supply. At this time the expedition was moving along the Sweetwater River. Small hunting expeditions were sent out each day to hunt buffalo. On one of these expeditions, Mose and his friend John Murphy went with two of the men, Joseph Foster and Allen Montgomery. During the course of the hunt the four hunters split up; Mose going in one direction with Allen Montgomery, while John Murphy and Joseph Foster went off in another direction.

At first it was very much like the unsuccessful hunt that Mose had been on before with John Murphy. The old bulls of the buffalo herd did sentry duty on high ground and warned the herd away when the hunters came close. The entire day was spent following the herd and never getting within rifle range.

Finally, when it was almost dark, the buffalo herd stopped by the Sweetwater River to drink. Mose and Allen dismounted and crawled toward the herd on their bellies, staying behind the cover of small bushes as much as possible. When they were close

to the herd, they opened fire, and killed nine buffalo. By that time it was too late to head back to camp, so they slept between the carcasses of the buffalo, while wolves circled around, howling and snarling, hungry for the buffalo meat. Mose and Allen kept a small campfire burning and the wolves did not attack.

Near morning, a huge bear chased the wolves away. The bear also was hungry for the buffalo meat. As soon as it was light enough to take aim, Mose and Allen tried to get a shot at the bear. But he fled, which was probably just as well, since a wounded bear is a dangerous animal.

Mose and Allen worked until three the next afternoon, carving the best slices of buffalo meat, and leaving the remains for the wolves. Then, with the meat packed on their horses, they started for camp. By nightfall, they still had not located the wagon train. They wandered in the night, walking and leading their tired horses, but they could find no familiar landmarks. It was morning when they finally found the wagon train. They stumbled into camp, exhausted, but loaded with meat. Probably Mose's success on this hunting expedition had a lot to do with the fact that he had an older, more experienced companion with him. He felt that the disgrace of his earlier failure was erased. John Murphy and Joseph Foster had been successful too, and John was grinning broadly. Now the two hunters who had once come back without their guns felt very victorious.

The pioneers stayed at their camp on the Sweetwater for a week, hunting buffalo and curing meat, to make sure that they would have a good supply of food for the trek across the desert lands to the west. At this camp, a daughter was born to Mr. and Mrs. James Miller of the California party. They named the girl

Ellen Independence Miller, after Independence Rock, a huge boulder that was a nearby landmark. Independence Rock was not the only jagged shape on the landscape. They were now high on the central plateau of North America, a land of strangely shaped boulders and spurs of red stone.

As the wagon train gradually climbed higher into the Rocky Mountains, the buffalo herds disappeared. However, there was a good supply of deer and antelope for the hunters, so there was no need to use the reserve supplies of cured buffalo meat.

They reached the summit of the Rockies in the middle of July. The waters of rivers and streams now ran down the mountains to the west. The pioneers were joyous, because they felt that their journey was nearing its end, and that the worst part of the trip was behind them. Later, they would discover how mistaken they had been in that feeling. But for the moment, everything seemed fine.

They camped at the Big Sandy River on the 21st and 22nd of July. There, Captain Stevens appointed "old man Hitchcock" as a guide. Mr. Hitchcock was an experienced pioneer who had been west before, and claimed that he knew the area better than anyone else. He suggested a cut-off that would take them westward to the Green River by a 25-mile route. Old Caleb Greenwood and his sons stood silently nearby, and listened to Mr. Hitchcock's suggestions. They did not like being replaced as guides.

The pioneers started out at dawn the next day. They moved across a dry barren land of sagebrush and great boulders. There was no water to be found. They moved stubbornly on all day. By nightfall, they had gone well over 25 miles, but they still had

not come to the Green River. People were starting to say unkind things about old Mr. Hitchcock. Finally, they had to stop
and camp. They were very tired and thirsty. The oxen were also
very thirsty and seemed to be suffering. About forty head of
oxen broke away during the night to search for water.

When morning came, everyone agreed that rather than
searching for the lost oxen they should drive on toward the
Green River. It was important to get water for themselves and
for the remaining oxen. Later they could send some riders back
to find the lost animals. So they started out as soon as it was
light, and by eleven o'clock they had reached the Green River.
There, the thirsty pioneers and their thirsty animals drank
deeply.

Six men were sent back to hunt for the lost oxen. Mose was
one of the six. But the six men did not stay together. Some of
them thought that the oxen would have headed toward the
nearest water, the Green River. The others thought that the
oxen would turn back to the last water they had seen, the Big
Sandy. Mose was one of those who thought that the oxen must
have returned to the Big Sandy. Therefore, he and John Murphy's older brother, Dan, and a Mr. Bean of the Oregon party
turned their horses eastward.

Half way to the Big Sandy, Dan Murphy, who was riding in
front, suddenly ducked low, slipped down to the side of his
horse, and motioned to the others to do the same. As Mose
clung to the side of his galloping horse, he could feel his heart
pounding with excitement. What was the matter? From his
awkward position, Mose drove his horse at full speed, to keep
up with Dan. Behind him, he could hear the rushing hooves of

Mr. Bean's horse. And as he hung there, being bounced and flung about like a saddle bag, he wondered: what did Dan see? Was it the Sioux?

It was the Sioux. When they came to a halt in a small canyon, Dan Murphy jumped to the ground. "Indians," he said.

The other two quickly dismounted, tied the horses to a tree, and crawled on their bellies to the top of the nearby hill. Before their eyes, the plain stretched to the horizon. In the middle of that plain was a war party of a hundred Sioux riding toward them.

The Sioux came closer, riding lightly on their horses. Mose and his friends hugged the ground, half hidden by the low brush and the rocks, not daring to move a muscle. Now the Indians were so close that Mose could hear them talking to one another in their harsh language. If one Indian decided to ride up the hill for some reason, the three pioneers were as good as dead. Mose kept his hands clenched on his rifle. Before his eyes, the painted, feathered Sioux rode by, only sixty feet away.

Finally, the last Sioux had passed them. But Mose and his friends stayed still for many minutes afterward, in case one of the Sioux scouts should glance behind him or circle back.

At last, they decided that they were safe. With sighs of relief they climbed onto their horses, and continued to ride eastward toward the Big Sandy.

At the Big Sandy they found the lost oxen grazing near the river banks as if they had lived there all their lives. They rounded them up, tied them securely, and slept that night beside the river.

The next morning, Mose and the other two men started to drive the cattle toward the Green River. They had gone a half a mile, when they saw two horsemen silhouetted against the sky on a distant hill. The two riders were Indians. Then, on another hill in the opposite direction, two more Indians appeared on horseback. Within ten minutes hundreds of Indians were visible, in all directions. The Indians were whooping and howling, and it was clear that they were about to charge. There was no way to escape. Daniel Murphy, Mr. Bean and Mose got down from their horses. They shook hands with each other and said goodbye, because they expected to be killed.

"They look like Sioux," said Mr. Bean.

Daniel Murphy nodded. "Wait till they get in range, and then fire. We'll get some of them."

"Maybe we should make friends with them," said Mose.

"They don't look very friendly, Mose," said Mr. Bean.

Mose nodded. It was true that the Indians did not look very friendly. As Mose watched them, he saw a few horsemen start

to move forward. Then, the whole war party came charging from all sides. Mose held his rifle ready.

But the charging Indians stopped well out of rifle range; and three of them came forward to talk, without weapons, and making peaceful signs with their hands. The hair on the back of Mose's neck had been standing straight out like quills, and the blood had been racing through his veins; but now he began to feel slightly calmer. Maybe there was a chance of making friends with these Indians after all.

The Indians were not Sioux. They turned out to be members of the Snake tribe. They were chasing after the Sioux war party that Mose and his friends had seen the day before. In spite of their initial wild charging and whooping, they were very friendly to the pioneers. Some of the Indians even stayed with Mose and his friends and helped them to drive the cattle back to Green River. But the main war party continued to ride after the Sioux, their deadly enemies.

Mose felt very triumphant when he arrived at the Green River camp at about nine o'clock that night, driving the lost cattle, with painted Indians at his side. It was better than being in a parade. Also, he was glad that he still had his scalp.

CHAPTER 5

The Rifle

THE WAGON TRAIN moved on toward the Bear River. There, the pioneers met with a famous old mountaineer named Pegleg Smith, who lived alone in the hills near the Bear River. He had lived a rough life in the Wild West and had amputated his own leg after it had been shattered by a bullet.

Pegleg Smith had several strong ponies, and he traded some of them for the tired horses in the wagon train. This trade was very helpful to the pioneers. And it may have been a profitable trade for Pegleg Smith, because the horses would be valuable to him after they were rested.

To the south, the Bear River ran into the Great Salt Lake. But the pioneers were bound in the opposite direction. Leaving

Pegleg Smith, the wagon train creaked northward along the river to Fort Hall. Fort Hall was a trading post at a fork in the trail, in the southeast part of what now is the state of Idaho. From Fort Hall, the Oregon wagons would take the trail to the northwest, while the smaller California party would take the trail to the southwest.

There were sad farewells at Fort Hall. Mose watched as the Oregon wagons rumbled into the distance. There went Mr. Derby who would not put out his fire, and Mr. Bean who had been with Dan Murphy and Mose when they had their close call with the Sioux war party, and many others whom Mose had been friendly with during the journey.

The eleven California wagons started out toward the southwest. In a few days they reached the Humboldt River, where they found a good supply of grass for the cattle. The wagon train followed the river for three hundred miles through land that is now the state of Nevada. For about two weeks they followed the winding banks of the Humboldt. And during this time, they met another tribe of Indians. These Indians were known to the pioneers as "Diggers" because they fed largely on roots that they dug out of the earth. But the pioneers were not very careful in the way they named the Indian tribes, and the Diggers were actually divided into two separate tribes: the Shoshones and the Paiutes. The first Diggers that Elisha Stevens and his people met were the Shoshones. Fortunately, Old Greenwood knew a few words of their language, so he was able to talk with the Indians.

There were Digger Indians around the wagon train all the way down the Humboldt. The pioneers noticed that these

Indians seemed to have very little energy. The Diggers usually did not have enough to eat, and that probably explained their weakened condition. The land near the Humboldt was not rich in food supplies. In fact, the Indians followed the wagon train mainly so that they could get food from the pioneers.

The Humboldt River ends in a swamp land called "the Humboldt Sink." The wagon trains halted there, and a camp was set up.

West of the Humboldt Sink lay a desert. The pioneers wanted to take the shortest possible route across that desert. There were some who thought that the best route would lie to the southwest. Others thought that they should go due west. There was much arguing about which route to take. Finally, an old Indian chief gave them some advice.

The old chief kept saying "truckee," and the pioneers thought that his name was Truckee. Actually, it was a word that meant "all right" in the chief's language. The chief was trying to be agreeable. But to the pioneers, he was Chief Truckee from that time on.

Nobody knew Truckee's language (he belonged to a Paiute tribe), so he and old Greenwood scratched pictures in the ground and made signs with their hands. From this silent conversation, old Greenwood was able to get the information about the land that lay to the west.

Old Greenwood wrinkled his brow and studied the marks in the dust. "It looks like there's a river about fifty or sixty miles due west," he said finally, looking up at Captain Stevens.

"Is the water good to drink?" asked Captain Stevens, thinking of the water of the Humboldt Sink which was bitter with alkali salts.

Old Greenwood and Truckee made drinking motions and more marks in the dust. Old Greenwood squinted carefully at the marks that Truckee made. Finally, he looked up at Captain Stevens again. "He says it's good water. It comes out of the mountains. Plenty of grass and trees, too."

But the pioneers decided to make sure that they took the right route. Suppose Truckee was lying or confused, or suppose that old Greenwood had misunderstood the marks in the dust — the wagon train might get lost in the desert.

Captain Stevens, Dr. Townsend, and Joseph Foster set out on horseback, with Truckee for a guide, to make sure that Truckee's information was correct. They were back at the camp three days later. They had good news — the river was where Truckee had said it was.

Although the pioneers found Truckee to be a helpful friend, there were troubles between pioneers and Indians at the Humboldt Sink camp. At first the Indians seemed friendly, although the pioneers kept an alert guard to make sure that nothing was stolen. But there was one man who was too suspicious of the Indians. That was John Greenwood. Although he was himself half-Indian, he had a vicious hatred of all Indians. Every time an ox strayed away from camp, John Greenwood was sure that the Indians had stolen it, even though all of the stray oxen were finally found. He was always ready to reach for his rifle, and it seemed as if he wanted very much to kill an Indian. The older men kept an eye on him at all times. Unless he were watched both day and night, who could know when he might fire a shot that would lead to an Indian war? And because of this one man's bloodthirsty feelings, everyone was uneasy. There was an electric feeling in the air, a feeling that anything could happen.

On the morning of October first, the wagon train was ready to move out. It was necessary to cross the mountain range to the west, the Sierra Nevada, before the heavy snows began. And it was then that the mistake was made that almost led to war. Strangely, it was not John Greenwood who made the mistake. It was Mose.

Mose was not a hater of Indians; he was very different from John Greenwood. For instance, he had enjoyed his meeting with the Snake Indians, when they helped to drive the cattle. But perhaps the tension in the camp and the hot-headed behavior of John Greenwood had put his nerves on edge.

The trouble came when Mose could not find the halter for his horse. With the wagons ready to move, Mose searched everywhere. Then, he saw the end of the halter sticking out beneath the feather blanket that one of the Indians was wearing. Mose asked the Indian to give him the halter.

The Indian ignored him.

Mose asked again for his halter, making signs so that the Indian would understand. But the Indian pretended not to understand.

Then Mose lost his temper, and grabbed the halter.

The Indian stepped back and drew his bow.

Mose ran to the wagon, seized his rifle, slid the bolt, and took aim at the Indian. But before he could pull the trigger, his rifle barrel was grabbed by a strong hand — grabbed so forcibly that

it was nearly wrenched from his grip. Mose found himself looking into the furious eyes of Martin Murphy.

All around, everyone was poised for battle. Pioneers had their
guns ready. Indians stood on all sides with drawn bows and
knives. Mose let go of his rifle and leaned weakly against the
wagon. He realized that in the heat of his temper he had almost
caused an Indian war. Every man, woman, and child in the
wagon train could have been slaughtered.

The leaders of the wagon train explained to the Indians what
had happened and gave them many presents in order to quiet
them. The Indians slowly put away their bows and arrows, and
accepted the presents. The pioneers lowered their rifles. Everyone drew deep breaths of relief.

Dr. Townsend had a long harsh lecture for Mose. But Mose felt so badly about what he had done that even the lecture did not make him feel much worse.

We do not know, from Mose's journal, what John Greenwood did during the excitement. But it seems likely that some husky pioneer must have grabbed him and held him until things quieted down. At any rate, John Greenwood did not kill an Indian that day. But history tells us that John Greenwood was a guide for another expedition a year later. On that expedition somewhere near the Humboldt, John Greenwood murdered an Indian in cold blood. After that, he was hunted as an outlaw by his fellow pioneers.

PART TWO

CALIFORNIA

CHAPTER 6

The Pass

WEST OF THE HUMBOLDT SINK, the pioneers spent two miserable, parched days crossing the desert. As Mose rode beside his wagon, after taking a turn driving the oxen, he looked out across the desert. As far as he could see, there was nothing but flat, scorched land, with an occasional spur of stone jutting up. The only things growing were joshua trees, cactus, and yucca plants. The wagons and the legs of the exhausted oxen were coated with dust. Old Greenwood was riding nearby, his nostrils and the lines in his face coated with dust. Even John and Brit Greenwood, riding at opposite sides of the wagon train, looked glum and weary, and showed few signs of their usual wild spirits.

Elisha Stevens was balanced on the tongue of his wagon, looking straight ahead into the distance, his tanned face streaked with sweat. Before him, his oxen strained and moaned as they pulled the rattling wagon across the sand.

Francis Deland, a rugged French Canadian, was taking a turn driving Dr. Townsend's oxen. Inside the covered wagon, Mose's sister was trying to sleep. But it was so hot that she could only turn restlessly from side to side. Dr. Townsend showed less discomfort from the heat than his wife did. He was spending his time cleaning and oiling a rifle that he had received in a trade at Fort Laramie. Mose could not understand why anyone would bother to clean a rifle in such a dusty place. It seemed as if it would need another cleaning as soon as the first cleaning was finished.

Even the younger children were quiet, most of them sleeping; a few perched on the edges of the wagons, staring sleepily into the clouds of dust thrown up by the creaking wheels. It was a weary company of people and animals that moved across the desert — far different from the merry crew that had set out from Council Bluffs so many months ago.

At two in the afternoon on the second day, they sighted the river. The thirsty animals were likely to stampede to the water, and the wagons would be broken to pieces. Therefore, the men quickly unhitched the oxen from the wagons. In honor of the helpful old Indian chief, they named the river *the Truckee*, and that is the name that it bears to this day.

For days the pioneers followed the winding Truckee. They

had to cross the river so often that they lost count of the number of times. But in one very difficult mile, they had to cross the Truckee .ten times. They were so tired that they would have liked to pitch camp for several days. But they could not risk taking a long rest. They had to cross the mountains before the heavy snowfalls. There was one pioneer, a Canadian named Dennis Martin, who did not seem very worried about snow. "I've lived half my life in snow," he said.

"Well," said Dan Murphy, "when the snow starts, I'll let our oxen go and let you pull the wagon."

By mid-October, they were still following the Truckee and there was already a light snowfall. The stream became narrower all the time, and the canyon which it ran through became deeper and more winding. The mountainous walls of the canyon became so steep and so close together that finally the oxen had to pull the wagons in the river bed itself. The oxen were exhausted, footsore, and starving. However, they were able to graze on the tips of plants that were sticking up out of the snow.

In mid-November, badly worn out, the pioneers came to a fork in the river. The main stream bore southwest, and the smaller stream bore due west. A meeting was held to decide which route to take. It was decided that they should split into two parties. If only one party reached California, they could send help to the other party.

The wagon train was to head west along the tributary. A smaller group on horseback would follow the Truckee to the southwest.

Six of the best riders were chosen for the horseback party. They were Dan Murphy, John Murphy, their twenty-year-old

sister Ellen Murphy, Mose's sister Elizabeth, and two French Canadians, Francis Deland and Oliver Magnent.

Captain Stevens shook hands with Dan Murphy. "We'll see you at Sutter's Fort, Dan. And if you don't see us there, send some help." Sutter's Fort, on the Sacramento River, was their first goal in California. John Sutter, the Swiss trader who

owned the fort, was said to be helpful to pioneers who came to California.

"You'll probably get to Sutter's before we do, Captain," said Dan Murphy.

Mose said goodbye to his sister and to his friends John and Dan Murphy. He wondered when and where he would see them again.

As the riders disappeared around a bend of the Truckee, the rest of the pioneers began to prepare a camp at the fork of the river. Their camp was close to the place where the town of Truckee now lies.

The wagon party broke camp the next day, and followed the smaller branch of the river for two miles until they came to a lake. There they camped again. The small river that they followed was named "Donner Creek" years later, and the lake is now known as "Donner Lake."

At Donner Lake, the canyon ended. To the west, there was a steep mountain wall. For several days everyone hiked in the mountains, searching for some pass that they could take the wagons through. Finally, they mapped out a rough trail.

Some of the men decided to leave their wagons behind. Only five of the eleven wagons would be taken across the Sierra Nevada. The other six would be left at the camp with a few men to guard them until help could be sent from Sutter's Fort.

The small wagon train, with its five wagons, started to move along the north side of the lake and up the mountain side. The snow was two feet deep now, and the climb was very hard. All supplies were taken out of the wagons, and carried by hand.

Double teams of oxen hauled the empty wagons up the steep
grade.

Halfway up the mountain, they came to a steep wall of rock
about ten feet high. There seemed to be no way through. The
pioneers searched the mountain side, looking for some break in
the rock wall. They had almost given up, when someone gave a
shout. There was a narrow break in the wall, barely wide
enough for one ox to pass through, and not wide enough for a
wagon.

The men unyoked the oxen and led them through in single
file. Then, using chains, they hitched some of the oxen to one

of the wagons ten feet below. With the oxen pulling from above, and with men pushing from below, they slowly moved the first wagon up and over the wall of rock. One by one, the wagons were hauled up the rock wall.

Those five wagons were the first to reach California from the east. Earlier parties had left their wagons on the eastern side of the Sierra Nevada range, and had gone into California on foot. Others went west to California on horseback. But none of the earlier expeditions had matched the feat of the Elisha Stevens party in bringing wagons across the Sierra Nevada.

The route that they had discovered through the mountains was to be famous. Through this pass, many wagon trains would follow in the years to come. Later, it was to be named "Donner Pass." The pass would be widened, and railroads and highways would be built through it. To this day, the Donner Pass is the main route for traffic between Nevada and California.

For the members of the Stevens party, the important fact was that they had made it across the Sierra Nevada, and now they were in California — ready to move on toward Sutter's Fort.

Three men were sent back to guard those wagons left at the camp, until more help could be sent. Those three men were Joseph Foster, Allen Montgomery, and Moses Schallenberger.

CHAPTER 7

The Cabin

MOSE WAS CHEERFUL as he and Joseph Foster and Allen Montgomery prepared to set up camp by the abandoned wagons. They kept little in the way of food supplies — only two exhausted, bony old oxen that were of no use to the wagon train. But they had their rifles, and were sure they could shoot enough game to feed them through the winter.

Their first task was to build a cabin that they could live in. They chopped down saplings, and used the two oxen to haul them. With the saplings, they built a rough, one-room cabin, about 14 feet long and 12 feet wide. Rawhides and pine brush were used to cover the cabin to keep the snow and the cold

wind from getting in. They even made a chimney of big logs. They cut a doorway in one wall, but they made no door, so the doorway was open all the time. That was good in one way — it gave them light during the daytime. The whole job took two days to finish. When they were done, the three men stood back and looked proudly at the results of their work.

That night Mose slept well, wrapped in two heavy blankets. He was exhausted from the two hard days of work and proud of the cabin that they had built so quickly. Also, he was looking forward to the next day, when they would hunt for game. He fell asleep wondering how the wagon train and the horseback party were doing, and looking forward to a winter of hunting and adventure.

Mose was disappointed the next morning. He was the first one up, and he went to the doorway to look out. It was snowing heavily. It was not a day for hunting.

"Don't worry about it, Mose," said Allen Montgomery. "We'll hunt tomorrow. It'll melt — you can tell from how warm it is."

But Allen Montgomery was wrong. They did not hunt the next day or the day after. The snow kept falling. For one week it snowed, while the three men stared gloomily out through the doorway. Finally, they had to kill the two oxen in order to eat, and Mose was relieved to see the starving oxen put out of their misery. They hung the meat up to freeze on the outside of the cabin and covered it with pine brush.

Day after day the snow fell. The little cabin was almost covered with snow. The snow was so soft that it would not hold up the weight of the men. Therefore, they could not leave the cabin, except on very short trips for firewood. When their supply of meat started to run low, Foster and Montgomery made snowshoes out of wagon bows and rawhide. Then, all three of them went hunting. Day after day they hunted. They saw nothing — not a single rabbit, or antelope or deer. Sometimes they saw the tracks of coyotes or foxes in the snow, but they never caught sight of the animals.

At last they realized that they faced slow starvation. There seemed to be only one hope for them — to continue toward Sutter's Fort on foot. Each of them took ten pounds of beef, his rifle, and a pair of blankets. Then they started out across the snow wearing their snowshoes.

But the snowshoes were not very well made. Furthermore, they mistakenly fastened the shoes with thongs at both the toe and the heel; they should have fastened them only at the toe, so that the heel could drag instead of having to be lifted at each step. As it was, the shoes sank into the snow, and with every step, each man was lifting pounds of snow on his snowshoes.

Mose was so exhausted from the difficult hike that he could hardly walk. His legs became cramped, and each step was agony for him. He was weak with hunger and suffering from frostbite. He fell down several times, and his companions had to wait until Mose's cramped legs recovered before continuing the hike. Finally, Mose was in such bad condition that they had to stop every fifty yards.

By sunset, they had reached the top of the mountain. A
short time later, they stopped and camped, chopping down a
tree to make a bonfire. The three men lay on beds of pine
branches, near the fire. But they were too exhausted to sleep.
Instead, they lay half-awake all night with aching legs, worry-
ing both about the members of the wagon train and about
themselves. All three of them knew that they might never
reach Sutter's Fort alive. And suppose the wagon train and the
horseback party were having the same kind of trouble — the
expedition that had started out so bravely from Council Bluffs
in the spring might never reach its goal.

In the morning, they saw the fire had melted the snow so
that it had sunk fifteen feet to the ground below. They sat by

the edge of the big pit, getting what warmth they could from the smoldering coals below and ate their beef. While they ate, they talked quietly about the journey that lay ahead of them. How could they best survive as they crossed that frozen wasteland?

Mose was the main problem. He was so stiff that he could hardly move. Montgomery and Foster did not think that Mose would be able to make the rest of the trip. Somewhere along the way, overcome by frostbite, cramps, and exhaustion, they would have to leave him to die. They were both powerful men, at the peak of their strengths. Mose was a thin boy of seventeen, already almost totally exhausted and unable to move. Montgomery and Foster could only shake their heads at the idea of Mose's going on.

But what other choice was there? "There's only one way," said Mose. "I'll go back to the cabin and live as long as I can on the beef that's there."

Sadly, his companions agreed with him. Here, in Moses Schallenberger's own words, written years later, is a description of how the men left:

We did not say much at parting. Our hearts were too full for that. There was simply a warm clasp of the hand accompanied by the familiar word, "Good-by," which we all felt might be the last words we should ever speak to each other. The feeling of loneliness that came over me as the two men turned away I cannot express, though it will never be forgotten; while the "Good-by, Mose," so sadly and reluctantly spoken, rings in my ears to-day.

CHAPTER 8

The Long Winter

STRANGELY, as soon as Mose was alone, he began to feel very hopeful. As he struggled back downhill for six frozen miles toward the cabin, he felt sure that he would be able to survive. Somehow, he told himself, I'll last.

The snow had frozen over during the night, forming a hard icy crust, so it was easier for him to walk. Nevertheless, he was so worn out by the time he arrived at the cabin that he was barely able to step over the nine-inch-high threshold of the cabin. He had to lift his leg with his hands to get it over the doorsill. The return trip had taken all day. It was nearly dark.

With his last ounces of strength, Mose built a fire and lay down
to sleep.

The next morning, Mose struggled over the snow to hunt. He
saw the tracks of many foxes, but he could not find a fox. He
came in, cold, miserable, and sick at heart that night. Once
more, it looked as if he faced starvation. But, as he put his gun
in the corner of the cabin, he caught sight of a gleaming piece
of metal. Several steel traps belonging to Elisha Stevens were

lying there. If I can't shoot a coyote or fox, why not trap one, thought Mose.

With new hope, Mose cut up the heads of the two oxen for bait, and put out several traps. Then he struggled back to the cabin and went to sleep. When morning came, he got up and went out right away to see if he had caught anything. He could hardly bear to look at the traps — if they did not work, and he had caught nothing — his chances to live would be very slight. If he had caught a fox or a rabbit, then there was a chance for life. To Mose's great joy, he found that he had trapped a coyote.

Mose roasted some of the coyote meat in a big pot from one of the covered wagons. He ate the meat, because he was starved, but it had a terrible taste. Next, he tried boiling the meat, but it was no better. He tried every way possible to cook the coyote, but nothing he did made it taste good. However, it was meat, and it did keep him alive. For three days it was his only food.

When Mose awoke on the fourth morning, he found that he had trapped two foxes. He roasted one of them, and was surprised to find that it had a delicious flavor. He was hungry enough to eat an entire fox in one day, but he carefully made each fox last for two days.

Now, considerably stronger and cheerier, Mose set out hunting again with his rifle. He never set eyes on any game, until he saw a crow perched on the branch of a tree. He took aim, fired, and brought down the crow. He hoped that crow might taste like chicken or turkey. He found that it tasted just as bad as coyote.

From then on, Mose forgot about the hunting and concentrated on trapping. He caught about one fox every other day, and that was enough to keep him alive and strong. Once in a while, he caught a coyote. But remembering the awful flavor of coyote meat, he hung these on the outside wall as a frozen food supply, in case he ever ran out of fox meat.

He had no other food but meat. But, somehow, he did not miss vegetables. He did have enough coffee for one cup. He saved that for Christmas day.

As the weeks passed, Mose felt more and more lonely and miserable. He had kept the leftover beef for another try at the westward hike, should the supply of foxes run out. Meanwhile, he kept trapping foxes and waiting for the end of winter. There were books in Dr. Townsend's wagon, and he would read these by the firelight every night. His favorite reading was *Lord Chesterfield's Letters to His Son*, and the poems of Byron. He would read aloud from those books, and that would make him feel less lonely. And sometimes he would talk out loud to himself. At night, as he fell asleep, he would wonder about his sister and about John Murphy and what had become of their horseback party. And he would wonder about the wagon train, and about Foster and Montgomery. When would he see them all again?

By late February, Mose had been in the cabin for almost three months. But it seemed as if years had gone by since he had seen or spoken with another human being.

Then, one evening just before sunset as he stood near the cabin looking across the snow, he saw someone coming. His pulse raced because for a moment he thought it was an Indian, and that he might have to fight for his life. Then, he recognized a familiar face. It was Dennis Martin from the wagon train, the Canadian who said he had lived half his life in the snow. He had come back to rescue Mose. Mose had never been so glad to see anybody in his whole life.

Mose welcomed Dennis Martin and invited him into the cabin. Dennis had news about the wagon train and horseback party. As they sat by the fire, gnawing on fox meat and warming their hands, Mose listened to every word that Dennis said — partly because he wanted to know about the others, and partly because he was so glad to hear someone's voice, besides his own.

CHAPTER 9

The Horseback Party

FIRST, DENNIS MARTIN told Mose about the horseback party. The story went something like this.

Upon leaving the wagon train, the four men and two women of the horseback party followed the Truckee River until they came to a large and beautiful lake. (That lake was later named Lake Tahoe. The six riders were the first pioneers to reach it.) They rode across the Truckee, staying on the west side of the lake, and crossed the mountains to the headwaters of the American River. Then, they followed the American River downhill to the lowlands. The American River was as crooked as the Truckee, but wider and deeper, and they had to cross it many times. Elizabeth Townsend was riding an Indian pony which was an excellent swimmer. She would ride him across the river, and then send him back with one of the boys to get Ellen Murphy, so that she also could have a safe ride across the river.

The Indian pony had crossed the river so many times that he was becoming exhausted. Finally, Mose's friend John Murphy was riding the pony across the river to get a pack saddle that had been left behind, when the tired pony lost his footing. John was thrown into the rushing waters and swept downstream. The force of the water bumped him against boulders, and even though he was a very good swimmer, he was too battered to swim. His brother and sister and the others watched helplessly from the shore, terrified for fear that John would be drowned. They rushed downstream, as John was swept out of sight. They all were chilled with fear that they would find his broken body washed up on the shore.

But John Murphy was looking after himself. Even while he was being hurled downstream by the tremendous power of the river, he was alert enough to sight a low-hanging branch overhead. As he was swept downstream, he lunged upward, and grabbed the branch with both hands. Then he hung there, holding on for dear life. The men got to him as fast as they could and helped him to shore. And there he fell unconscious — the icy waters and the bumps he had suffered from the rocks had weakened him greatly. They warmed him by the fire and brought him back to consciousness. But he was still badly shocked from his experience. They camped there by the river to give him time to recover. It was several days before John was his usual adventurous self.

For three weeks, they rode their horses along the American River. Finally, they were out of the mountains and were in the great Sacramento Valley. There they found herds of cattle. The men killed calves, and everyone ate well.

At last, they came to a big ranch. They had arrived at an outpost of civilization in California. The ranch belonged to a

74

Mr. and Mrs. Sinclair. The Sinclairs welcomed the adventurers, gave them sleeping quarters and fed them well. Like most other American settlers in California, the Sinclairs had come west by ship around Cape Horn. They were fascinated by the tales of hardship that they heard from these pioneers who had crossed the Sierra Nevada.

But the pioneers were feeling guilty. They were afraid that the calves they had killed belonged to the Sinclairs. It made them feel that they had taken advantage of their hosts. It was true that they had hunted the cattle at a time of great need, when they came out of the wilderness hungry and trail-worn. But they still did not feel right about it. Finally, they drew straws to see who would confess to the Sinclairs. Dan Murphy drew the short straw.

The next night at the dinner table, Dan Murphy cleared his throat awkwardly and asked the Sinclairs who owned the cattle along the river.

Mr. Sinclair said that he guessed they were all his.

"Well," said Dan, "there's a good bunch of them. What are calves about three months old worth in this country?"

Mr. Sinclair told him.

"Well," said Dan, talking very quickly, "we killed some of them to eat and we haven't got any money to pay you now; but if you will let us work out the price, we will be very much obliged."

Mr. Sinclair laughed. He told Dan Murphy that they were welcome to the calf meat, and that they could kill as many more as they wanted.

After hearing that, the pioneers felt much more relaxed at the ranch. But they could not stay too long. They were anxious to reach Sutter's Fort, where they hoped to meet with the wagon train.

Sutter's Fort was a colony founded by John A. Sutter. Sutter was born in Switzerland in 1803. He was an adventurous man whose wanderings finally took him to California in the year 1840.

Sutter was not only an adventurous wanderer, he was also an adventurous business man. There were Russian settlers in California who had been carrying on a large fur trade. But in 1840 these settlers were ordered back to Russia by their government. Sutter decided to buy them out. From the Russians, Sutter bought cattle and horses, a small ship, cannons, muskets, and the charter to the fur trade.

Sutter shipped the cannons and muskets up the Sacramento River to the location where he wanted to start his colony. There, with the help of Indians and American pioneers, he built his fort.

At this time, California was still owned by Mexico. The Mexican government did not like the looks of the cannons and muskets that Sutter was taking to his colony. It seemed that he was becoming a military force in California. But Manuel Micheltorena, the new Mexican governor of California, was a peaceful man, skilled in settling quarrels between men or between nations. He was able to keep peace between the Mexican government and John Sutter.

As the years went by, almost all American pioneers arriving in northern California went to Sutter's Fort. Sutter was quick to welcome the pioneers, and Sutter's Fort became an important American settlement in a foreign land.

But there was to be trouble. Many Spanish Californians did not trust Sutter and the American pioneers. And they did not trust Micheltorena, partly because of his friendship with the pioneers. In the winter of 1844, they rebelled against Micheltorena. There was civil war in the Mexican province of California.

When the four men and two women of the horseback party arrived at Sutter's Fort, that civil war had just broken out.

At about the same time that the horseback party reached Sutter's Fort, the men from the wagon train arrived on horseback.

"Where are the wagons?" asked Elizabeth Townsend, when she saw Captain Stevens.

"We had to leave them at the Yuba River, Ma'am, this side of the pass. Snowed in. The women and children stayed with them, and Mr. Murphy's taking care of them."

When Elizabeth saw her husband, she ran to embrace him. "John," she said, "where's my brother?"

"Mose stayed behind," said Dr. Townsend. "He's guarding our wagons east of the pass. Don't worry, we'll get him soon — when we go back for the others, we'll get him too."

But the pioneers were not able to go back to rescue their families at the Yuba River and Mose in his snowbound cabin. John Sutter was organizing a small "army" to help Governor Micheltorena. On January 1, 1845, "Sutter's army" rode south. Captain Stevens, the Murphy boys, and the other men from the covered wagons were given muskets and were made part of Sutter's army. Doctor Townsend was the company surgeon. They rode with Sutter's army south to Santa Barbara, and for two months, the families at the Yuba and Mose in his cabin waited in the snow. But no help came.

Then, Sutter decided that he did not need the men from the Stevens party after all. In February, the men of the wagon train were free to go back for the people whom they had left in the Sierra Nevada. At the request of Mose's sister, Dennis Martin went beyond the Yuba River camp to rescue Mose.

CHAPTER 10

The Camp at Bear River

AFTER MOSE HEARD from Dennis Martin about the adventures of his friends, the two men had a good night's sleep in the cabin. The next morning, Dennis made Mose a good pair of snow-shoes, like the ones he himself was wearing, and the two of them started toward the west on foot. Before he left, Mose looked back at the snowbound cabin where he had struggled against frost and starvation for so many months. It was a place that he would never forget. He was glad to be leaving the cabin alive.

Mose was weak from his hungry winter, but with Dennis Martin's help, he was able to climb the pass and hike to the

Yuba River. There the five wagons and the women and children waited. Most of the men of the wagon train had come back from Sutter's Fort to help in the rescue.* Mose was glad to see his friend John Murphy again. Before long, Mose and John were exploring around the camp the way they used to do on the prairies. But both of them had changed during the journey. They had been through the ordeals and struggles of manhood.

The pioneers waited for a few days before leaving the Yuba camp, because a child was born there. The child was a girl, born to Mr. and Mrs. Martin Murphy. They named her Elizabeth. When they did break camp, Elizabeth was carried in a basket that was attached to the pommel of her mother's saddle. But as they crossed the Yuba, the basket slipped off and fell into the river. Martin Murphy dove into the water and came up soaked, but with his crying daughter safe in his arms. After that, the little girl was given the middle name "Yuba," and was known from then on as Elizabeth Yuba Murphy.

With the wagon train was a man named Neil, who had come from Sutter's Fort with horses and supplies. Strengthened by food that Neil had brought, the pioneers drove on. On March 1, just one year from the time they left Council Bluffs, they camped by the banks of the Bear River** in California.

It was raining heavily, and as a result the Bear River was full and overflowing its banks. The melting snows were adding

* Joseph Foster and Allen Montgomery are not mentioned again in Mose's journal. But they may have been at the Yuba River camp.

**Not to be confused with the Bear River that the wagon train followed seven months earlier on the way to Fort Hall in Idaho.

to the waters of the flooded river. There was neither a bridge across the river nor a ferryboat, and it was far too dangerous to ride the horses across the swollen river. At last, the leaders of the wagon train decided that a large tree should be chopped down and used as a bridge. Everyone searched about for a tree large enough.

Then, there was an accident. Mr. Neil was cut off by the overflowing waters. He found himself on a strip of land with water on all sides. And he did not know how to swim. The waters kept rising and Mr. Neil had to climb a small tree.

Mose and John Murphy leaped onto their horses, and leading a third horse, they rode into the angry river to rescue Mr. Neil. It was strange that Mose and John so often found themselves in the midst of every danger. Perhaps it was because they were young and adventurous and eager for action. John Murphy's accident in the American River and Mose's ordeal in the cabin had not crushed their courage and their spirit. They rescued Mr. Neil before any of the older men in camp had time to move.

The flood became worse. The pioneers had to draw their wagons back into the hills. Soon the flooding river was ten miles wide. All of the food that Sutter had sent had been eaten, and everyone was very hungry. Two deer were killed, and each pioneer was given a small piece of venison. Then, for three days there was almost no food at all. To make matters worse, the pioneers could see large herds of cattle on the far side of the river. But there was no way to get to them.

Mose sat sadly on the tongue of a wagon and whittled a stick, thinking about his empty stomach — a stomach that had

been empty so often over the last few months that a good meal
was a strange and unusual experience.

There was a four-year-old boy named Barney in the Murphy
family. He walked up to Mose and asked Mose to let him use
his knife.

"Certainly," said Mose, "but what do you want to do with
it?"

Barney said, "I want to make a toothpick."

Mose was amused to hear little Barney talking about toothpicks when nobody had eaten for days. Certainly there was no shred of meat between anybody's teeth, and if ever there were people who had no need for a toothpick, they were the people. Mose had a good laugh and for a moment forgot about his hunger.

But the hunger pains came back quickly enough. Mose was not the only one who was starving. Some of the men were talking about killing a wild horse, because there were a number of them nearby. In those days, when horses were so important to people, nobody liked the idea of shooting a horse. However, when people are faced with starvation, they are ready to do things which they would not usually do.

But Martin Murphy objected. He refused to have anything to do with the shooting and eating of horses. He told the others to be patient — he would ride back into the hills to see if he could find an ox that had been lost on the march. Then they could all have a good feast. Mounting his horse, he rode off into the hills with his rifle.

Mose and Dennis Martin also went hunting, nearer to camp. They found nothing but wild horses. Finally, in spite of Martin Murphy, they decided that wild horse meat was their only hope. Mose aimed his rifle and brought down a fat horse. Everyone worked quickly to slice up the horsemeat and to cook it before Martin Murphy came back to camp.

When Martin Murphy returned, empty-handed, he saw the meat roasting by the fire. He smiled happily. "Who killed the heifer?"

Someone pointed to Mose.

Martin Murphy patted Mose on the shoulder. "Good boy, good boy, but for you we might all have starved."

When everyone sat down to eat, nobody had a better appetite than Martin Murphy. Between mouthfuls he talked about the meat — How juicy it was! How tender it was! What a fine flavor!

Then, when the dinner was over, one of the men pulled the horse's mane from behind a log and showed it to Martin Murphy. When he understood what he had eaten, he became quite ill. Later he said that he thought the meat had a bad taste. Never again, so long as he lived, did anyone trick him into eating horsemeat. That was understandable. He was undoubtedly a man who loved horses.

Soon, the rain stopped, and the flood-waters receded. Then the river was shallow enough to allow the pioneers to cross, and they reached the Feather River. There, Sutter supplied a boat to ferry them across; *vaqueros* (Mexican cowboys) brought them a fat cow, and they all had what Mose called their first good square meal in many months.

The long, dangerous trip was over. They had all arrived in California alive and in good health. Now they could begin the new life that they had crossed a continent to find. Mose was sure that it would be worth all the hardships of the trail.

CHAPTER 11

A New Land

THE MEMBERS OF the Stevens expedition went their separate ways in California. But they had helped to pave the way for other pioneers who were to follow. A few years after the Stevens expedition, so many American pioneers had come to California that California became a state in the union. And now trains, automobiles, and buses still bring people to California through the Donner Pass.

As to Captain Elisha Stevens who headed the expedition, he was a lonely man who liked to live by himself. For a short time, he worked at his blacksmith's trade in the old Spanish city of Monterey, California. Later, he lived as a trapper in the hills of Santa Clara County. Stevens Creek, which runs from those hills into San Francisco Bay, was named for him. Finally, he moved inland and farther south to live on a ranch; that area is now part of the city of Bakersfield.

The Murphy family settled in Santa Clara County. John Murphy's father started a cattle ranch south of San Jose near the present city of Gilroy. John's brother, Martin, also staked out a farm in Santa Clara County. Later, a small town grew about the Martin Murphy farm. That town was named Murphy. Over the years its name changed several times: it became Murphy's Station; then Encina; then Encinal, and finally Sunnyvale, which is the name it bears today.

Mose's friend John Murphy, who was so full of mischief and adventure in 1844, must have quieted down in later years, because he became the mayor of the city of San Jose. However, he did have another adventure first, in which he found gold in the Sierra Nevada. And little Barney Murphy, who asked Mose for a toothpick, eventually became the president of a San Jose bank.

We even hear more of the old Indian chief, Truckee. He was helpful to other people in later years, drawing his maps in the dust to show them the trail west. And those later pioneers continued to call him by the mistaken name "Truckee." Truckee's granddaughter, Sarah Winnemucca Hopkins, wrote a book years later, entitled *Life Among the Paiutes.*

John and Elizabeth Townsend bought a farm in San Jose. There, both of them died in 1850 at a fairly young age, leaving behind an infant son. Mose moved to the San Jose farm, adopted his orphaned nephew, and brought the boy up as if he were his own son. Later, Mose married a Miss Fanny Everitt, and they had five children. One of Mose's daughters, Maggie, became a teacher and a very learned woman; and when her father told her the story of his journey of 1844, she wrote down his words. From the story that Moses Schallenberger told his daughter, the overland journey has become history.

Mose and the others who came west with him in 1844 were brave people, full of the spirit of adventure. From the deeds of those people and people like them, the United States of America has become a great nation, stretching across a continent from one ocean to another.

A tintype of Elisha Stevens taken many years after his epic wagon journey.

*Gray's portrait of
Martin Murphy in
later years.*

Gray

Index

The Author

MICHAEL CHESTER received his training at the University of California at Berkeley and is now a research specialist to the missile industry. It was at Berkeley that the author took a creative writing course taught by Professor George Stewart, author of a work on the overland journey to California. This was the beginning of Mr. Chester's interest in California history and blazed the trail for his own work.

The author has written and co-written many juvenile books for Putnam, mainly on rockets and space. His latest books are *Robots in Space,* and *Let's Go to the Moon.*

Mr. Chester, his wife and three children live in Sunnyvale, California.